The Easy Key

Showtunes Vol 1
23 classic songs for keyboard

Published 1994

Music arranged & processed by Barnes Music Engraving Ltd East Sussex TN34 1HA

© International Music Publications Ltd
Griffin House 161 Hammersmith Road London England W6 8BS

All Of You

Words & Music by Cole Porter

Suggested Registration: Vibraphone
Rhythm: Slow Swing
Tempo: ♩ = 88

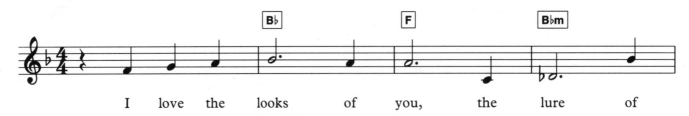

I love the looks of you, the lure of

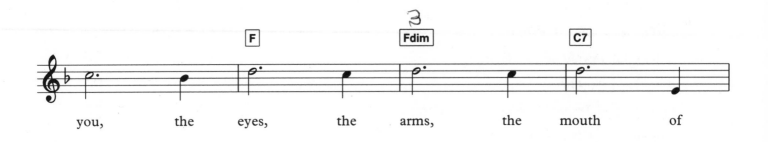

you. I'd love to make a tour of

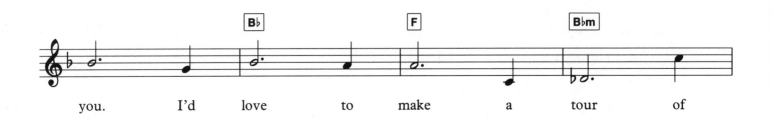

you, the eyes, the arms, the mouth of

you. The east, west, north and the south of you.___

___ I'd love to gain com - plete con - trol of

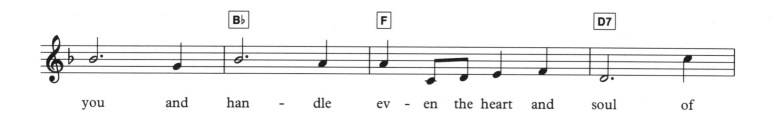

you and han - dle ev - en the heart and soul of

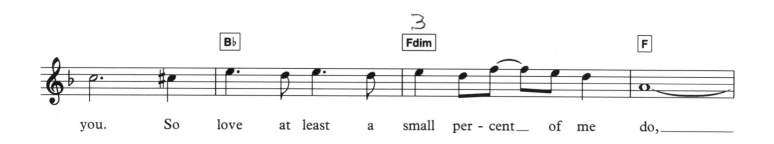

you. So love at least a small per - cent__ of me do,_____

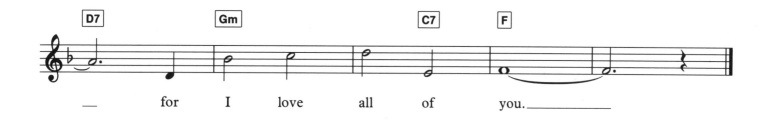

__ for I love all of you._____

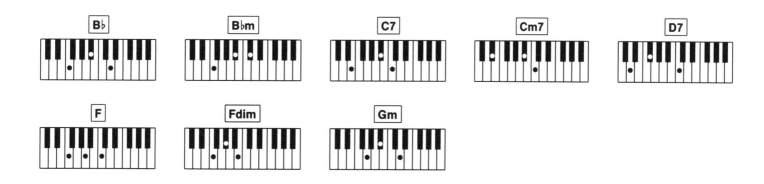

Anything Goes

Words & Music by Cole Porter

Suggested Registration: Vibraphone
Rhythm: Swing
Tempo: ♩ = 170

In old - en days a glimpse of stock - ing was

looked on as some - thing shock - ing, but now God knows,____

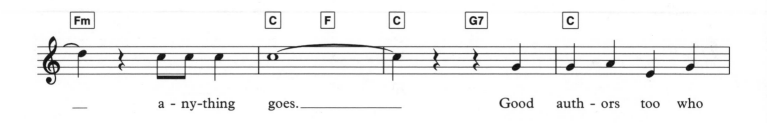

_ a - ny-thing goes.____ Good auth - ors too who

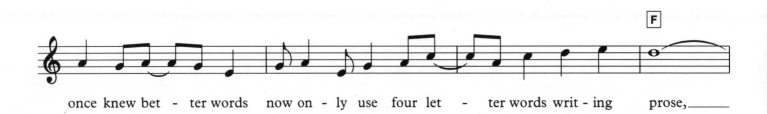

once knew bet - ter words now on - ly use four let - ter words writ - ing prose,____

_ a - ny-thing goes. The world has gone mad to - day,_ and good's

bad to - day, and black's white to - day,__ and day's night to - day.__ When most

guys to - day__ that wo - men prize to - day__ are just sil - ly gi - go - los.__

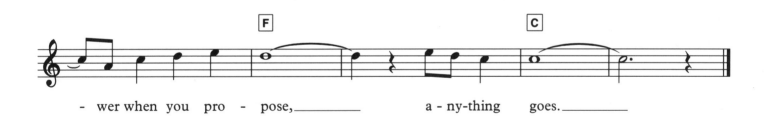

__ So though I'm not a great ro - man - cer, I know that I'm bound to ans -

- wer when you pro - pose,_____ a - ny - thing goes._____

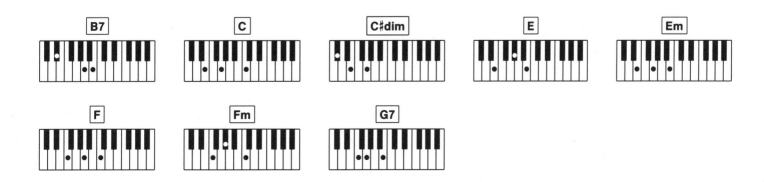

Embraceable You

Music and Lyrics by George Gershwin and Ira Gershwin

Suggested Registration: Piano
Rhythm: Swing
Tempo: ♩ = 104

Em - brace me my sweet, em - brace - a - ble you._____

Em - brace me you ir - re - place - a - ble you._____

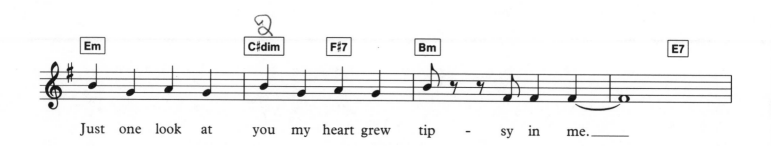

Just one look at you my heart grew tip - sy in me._____

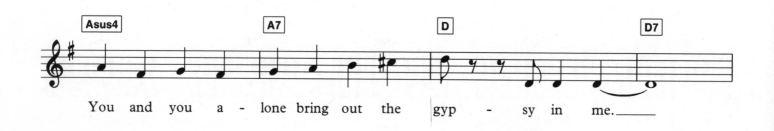

You and you a - lone bring out the gyp - sy in me._____

I love all the ma-ny charms a-bout you.____

A-bove all I want my arms a-bout you.____

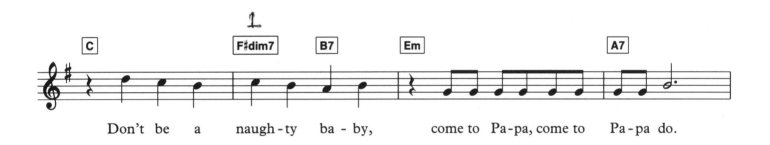

Don't be a naugh-ty ba-by, come to Pa-pa, come to Pa-pa do.

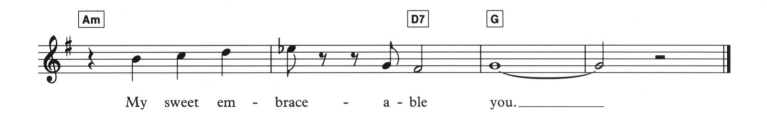

My sweet em-brace - a-ble you._____

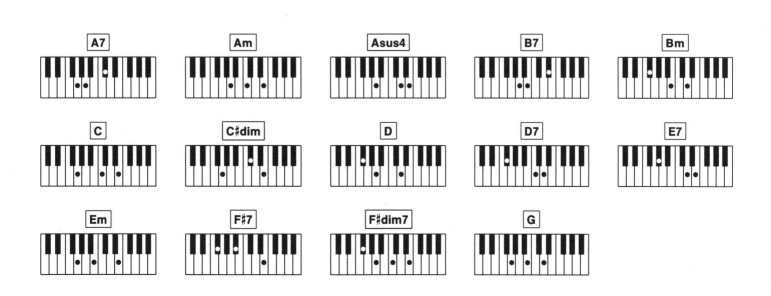

Forty-Second Street

Words by Al Dubin / Music by Harry Warren

Suggested Registration: Piano
Rhythm: Dixie Swing
Tempo: ♩ = 122

Come and meet_____ those danc - ing feet,_____ on the a - ve - nue I'm tak-ing you to,__ For - ty - se-cond street.

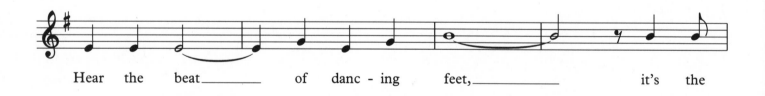

Hear the beat_____ of danc - ing feet,_____ it's the song I love the me - lo - dy of,__ For - ty - se-cond street.

Lit – tle "nif-ties" from the fif-ties, in – no – cent and sweet.

Se – xy la-dies from the eigh-ties, who are in – dis – creet. They're side by side,___

__ they're glo – ri – fied,_____ where the un – der-world can meet the e – lite,_

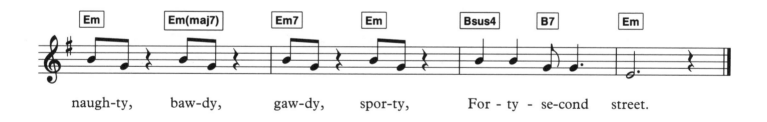

naugh-ty, baw-dy, gaw-dy, spor-ty, For – ty – se-cond street.

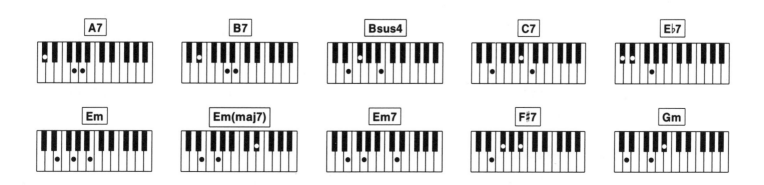

I Am What I Am

Words & Music by Jerry Herman

Suggested Registration: Piano
Rhythm: 8 beat
Tempo: ♩ = 96

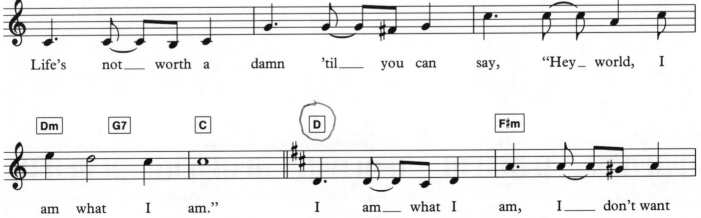

I Could Have Danced All Night

Words by Alan Jay Lerner / Music by Frederick Loewe

Suggested Registration: Vibraphone
Rhythm: Beguine
Tempo: ♩ = 126

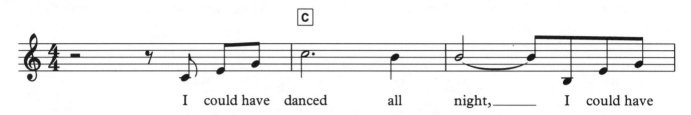

I could have danced all night,_____ I could have

danced all night, and still have begged for more._____

_ I could have spread my wings_____ and done a

thou - sand things, I've ne - ver done be - fore._____

_ I'll ne - ver know_____ what made it so ex - cit - ing._____

_____ Why all at once my heart took flight.

I on-ly know when he_____ be-gan to dance with

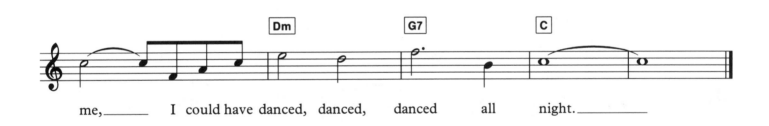

me,_____ I could have danced, danced, danced all night._____

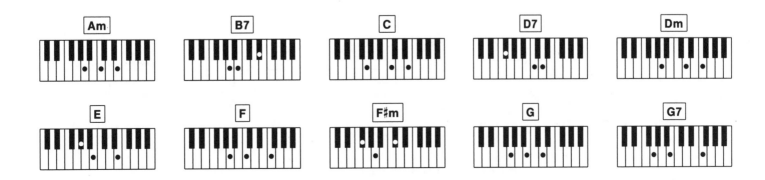

IF I RULED THE WORLD

Words by Leslie Bricusse / Music by Cyril Ornadel

Suggested Registration: Piano
Rhythm: Soft Rock
Tempo: ♩ = 80

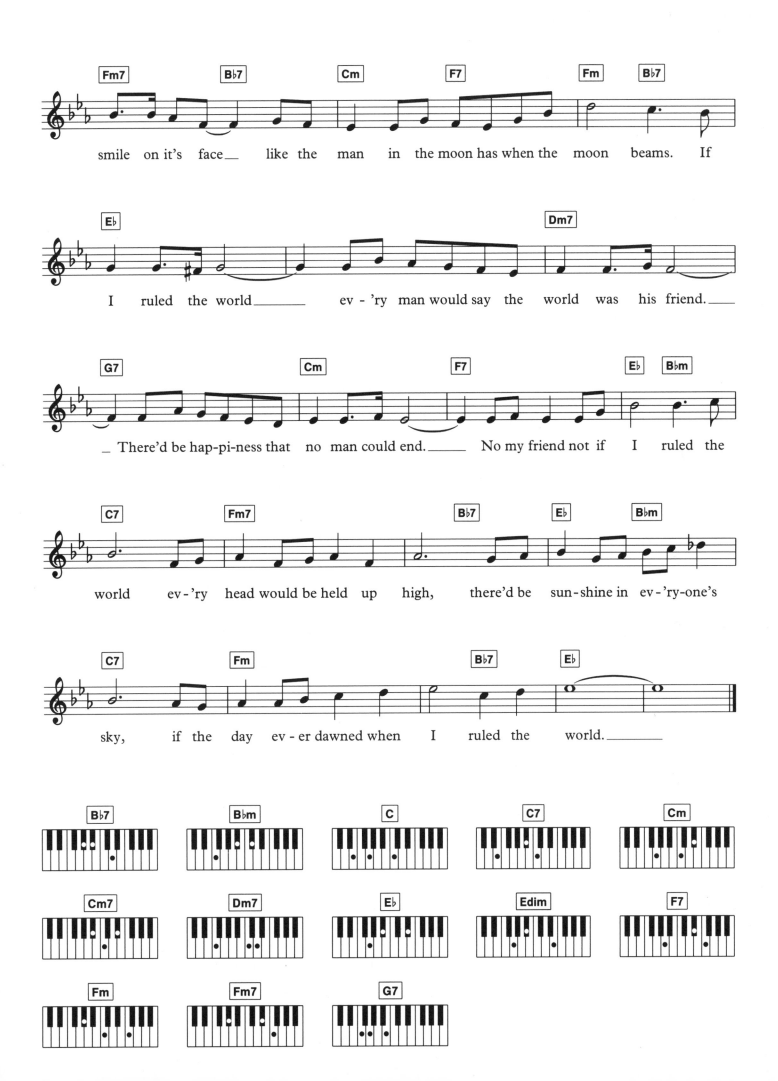

I Get A Kick Out Of You

Words & Music by Cole Porter

Suggested Registration: Vibraphone
Rhythm: Swing
Tempo: ♩ = 132 (♩ = 66 for melody)

I Got Rhythm

Music and Lyrics by George Gershwin and Ira Gershwin

Suggested Registration: Vibraphone
Rhythm: Swing
Tempo: ♩ = 144

I _____ got rhy - thm, I _____ got mu - sic, _____

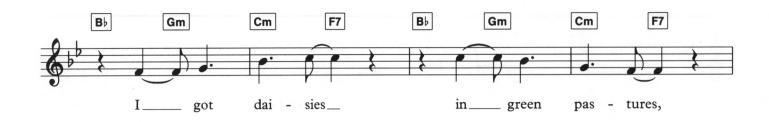

I _____ got my man, who could ask for a - ny-thing more?

I _____ got dai - sies _____ in _____ green pas - tures,

I _____ got my man, _ who could ask for a - ny-thing more?

Old _____ man trou - ble, _____ I _____ don't

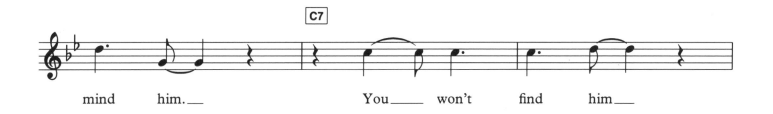

mind him.___ You___ won't find him___

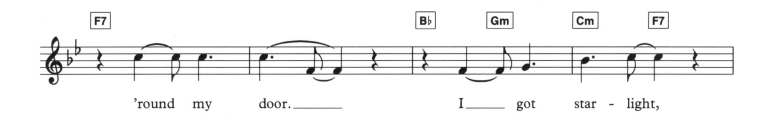

'round my door._____ I___ got star - light,

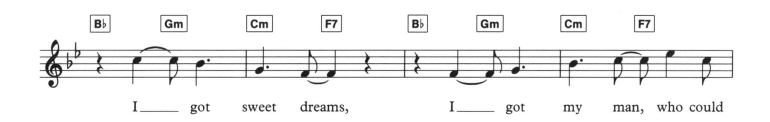

I___ got sweet dreams, I___ got my man, who could

ask for a - ny-thing more, who could ask for a - ny-thing more?

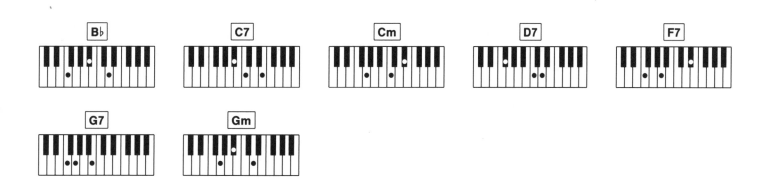

I Love Paris

Words & Music by Cole Porter

Suggested Registration: Vibraphone
Rhythm: Swing / Fox Trot
Tempo: ♩ = 94

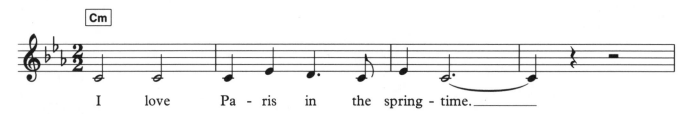

I love Pa - ris in the spring - time._____

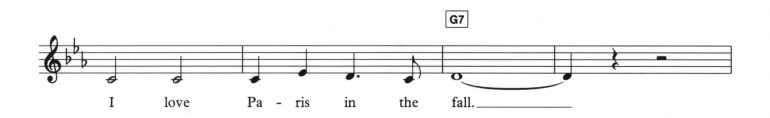

I love Pa - ris in the fall._____

I love Pa - ris in the win - ter when it driz - zles.

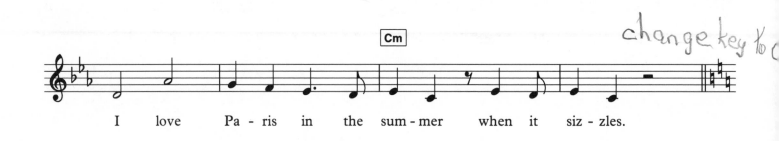

I love Pa - ris in the sum - mer when it siz - zles.

change key to C

I love Pa - ris ev - 'ry mo - ment,_____

ev - 'ry mo - ment of the year._____

I love Pa - ris. Why, oh why do I love Pa - ris?

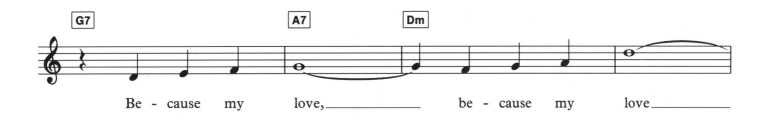

Be - cause my love,_____ be - cause my love_____

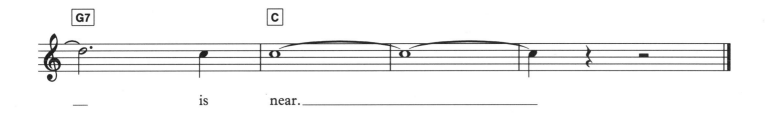

__ is near._____

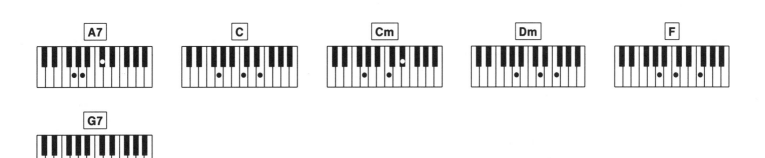

I Remember It Well

Words by Alan Jay Lerner / Music by Frederick Loewe

Suggested Registration: Accordian
Rhythm: Waltz
Tempo: ♩ = 106

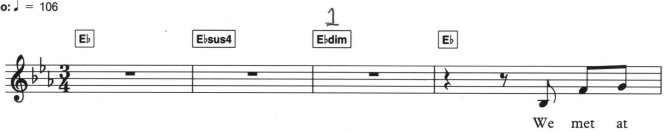

We met at

nine. (We meet at eight.) I was on time. (No you were late.) Ah

yes, I re - mem - ber it well. We dined with

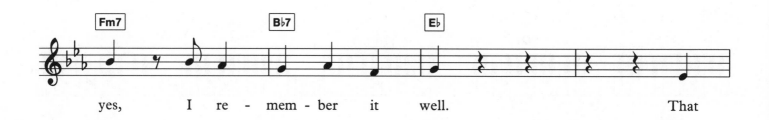

friends. (We dined a - lone.) A te - nor sang. (A ba - ri - tone.) Ah

yes, I re - mem - ber it well. That

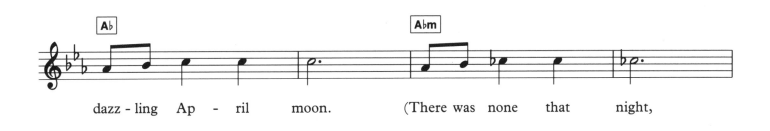

dazz - ling Ap - ril moon. (There was none that night,

and the month was June.) That's right, that's right. (It warms my

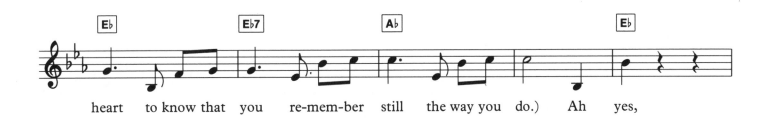

heart to know that you re-mem-ber still the way you do.) Ah yes,

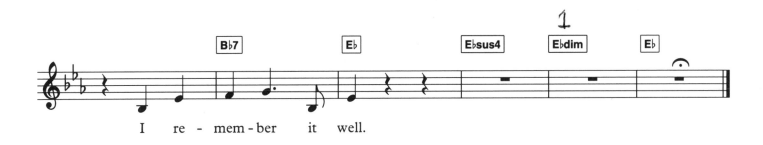

I re - mem - ber it well.

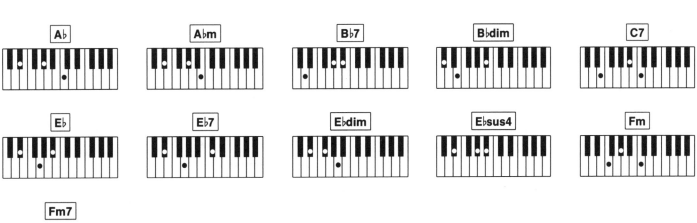

It Might As Well Be Spring

Words by Oscar Hammerstein II / Music by Richard Rodgers

Suggested Registration: Jazz Guitar
Rhythm: Slow Swing / Ballad
Tempo: ♩ = 72

It's De-Lovely

Words & Music by Cole Porter

Suggested Registration: Vibraphone
Rhythm: Swing
Tempo: ♩ = 132

The night is young, the skies are clear and if you want to go

walk-ing dear, it's de-light-ful,_ it's de-li-cious, it's de-love-ly._

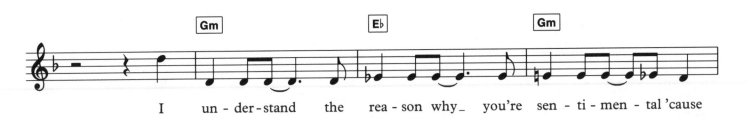

I un-der-stand the rea-son why_ you're sen-ti-men-tal 'cause

so am I,_ it's de-light-ful,_ it's de-li-cious, it's de-love-ly._

You can tell at a glance what a swell night this

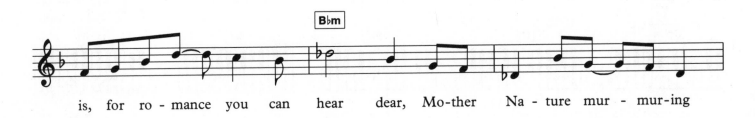

is, for ro-mance you can hear dear, Mo-ther Na-ture mur-mur-ing

low,   "Let your-self go." So please be sweet my chick - a - dee, __ and

when I kiss __ you just say to me, __ it's de - light - ful, __ it's de -

- li - cious, it's de - lect - a - ble, __ it's de - li - ri - ous, __ it's di -

- lem - ma, it's __ de - li - mit,   it's de - luxe, it's de - love - ly. __

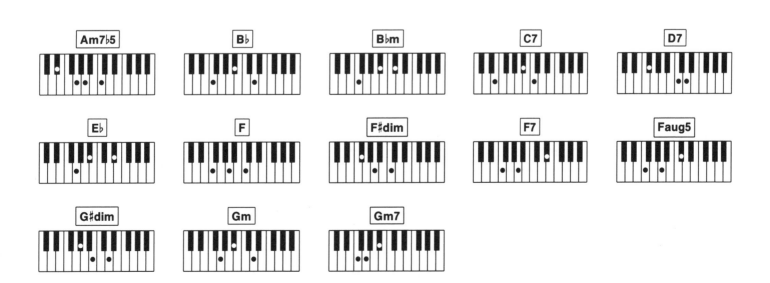

Let's Call The Whole Thing Off

Music and Lyrics by George Gershwin and Ira Gershwin

Suggested Registration: Vibraphone
Rhythm: Swing
Tempo: ♩ = 108

You say ee - ther and I say eye - ther. You say nee - ther and I say nye - ther.

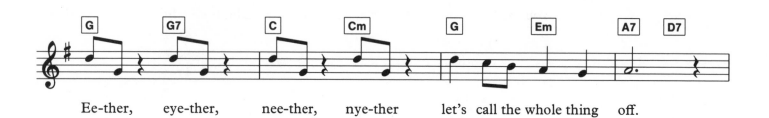

Ee-ther, eye-ther, nee-ther, nye-ther let's call the whole thing off.

You like po-ta-to and I like po-tah-to. You like to-ma-to and I like to-mah-to. Po -

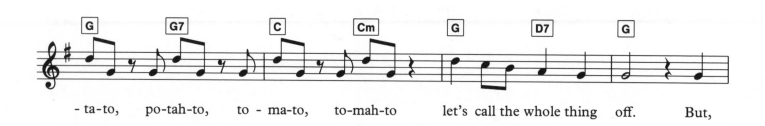

-ta-to, po-tah-to, to - ma-to, to-mah-to let's call the whole thing off. But,

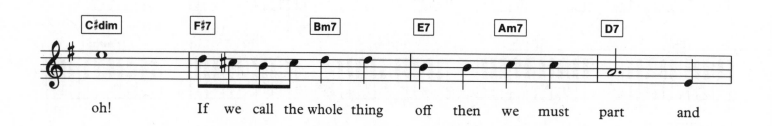

oh! If we call the whole thing off then we must part and

oh, if we ev-er part then that might break my heart. So if

you like pa-ja-mas and I like pa-jah-mas, I'll wear pa-ja-mas and

give up pa-jah-mas. For we know we need each oth-er, so we

bet-ter call the call-ing off off. Let's call the whole thing off.

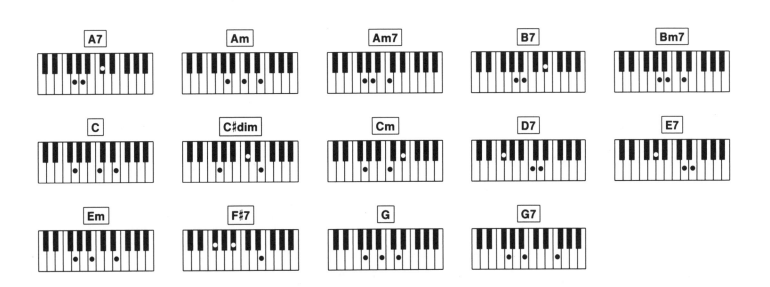

LULLABY OF BROADWAY

Words by Al Dubin / Music by Harry Warren

Suggested Registration: Vibraphone
Rhythm: Swing
Tempo: ♩ = 124

Come on a-long and lis-ten to ___ the lul-la-by of Broad-way.

The hip hoo-ray and bal-ly - hoo, ___ the lul-la-by of Broad-way.

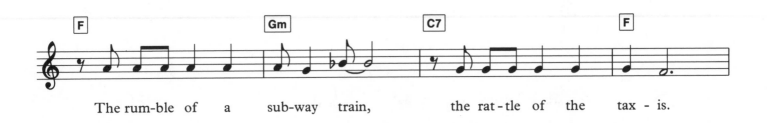

The rum-ble of a sub-way train, the rat-tle of the tax - is.

The daf-fy-dils who en-ter - tain ___ at An-ge-los and Max-ies. When a

Broad-way ba - by says, "Good - night," it's ear - ly in the morn - ing.

MY FUNNY VALENTINE

Words by Lorenz Hart / Music by Richard Rodgers

Suggested Registration: Vibraphone
Rhythm: Slow Swing
Tempo: ♩ = 78-84

My fun - ny Val - en-tine, sweet, co - mic Va - len-tine.

You make me smile with my heart._____

Your looks are laugh - a - ble, un - pho - to - graph - a - ble.

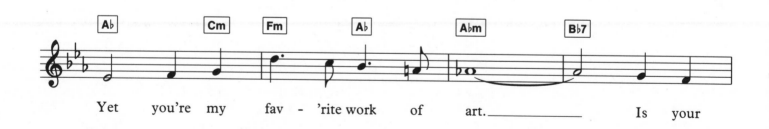

Yet you're my fav - 'rite work of art._____ Is your

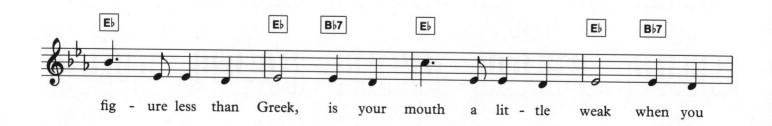

fig - ure less than Greek, is your mouth a lit - tle weak when you

op - en it to speak. Are you smart?_____ But

don't change a hair for me, not if you care for me.

Stay lit - tle Val - en - tine, stay._____

Each day is Val - en - tine's day._____

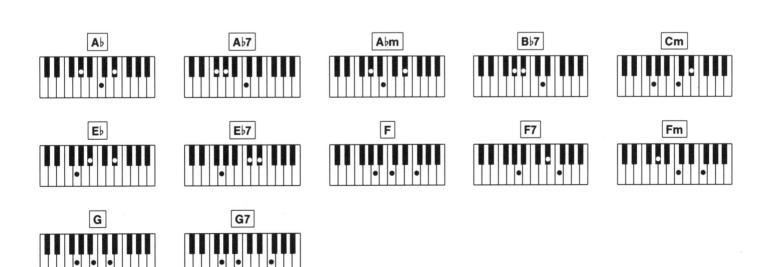

Summer Nights

Words & Music by Warren Casey and Jim Jacobs

Suggested Registration: Piano
Rhythm: Pop (8 beat)
Tempo: ♩ = 104

Sum-mer lov-in' had me a blast.__ Sum-mer lov-in'

hap-pened so fast.__ Met a girl, cra-zy for me.__

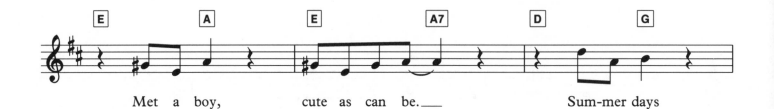

Met a boy, cute as can be.__ Sum-mer days

drift-ing a-way__ too__ uh, oh those sum-mer nights.__ Well-a, well-a, well-a,

uh. Tell me more, tell me more. Did you get ve-ry far?__ Tell me more, tell me

The Sun Has Got His Hat On

Words & Music by Ralph Butler and Noel Gay

Suggested Registration: Piano
Rhythm: Dixie
Tempo: ♩ = 160

The

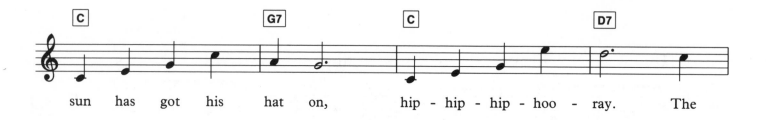

sun has got his hat on, hip - hip - hip - hoo - ray. The

sun has got his hat on and he's com - ing out to - day.

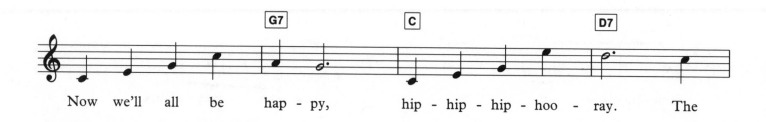

Now we'll all be hap - py, hip - hip - hip - hoo - ray. The

sun has got his hat on and he's com - ing out to - day.

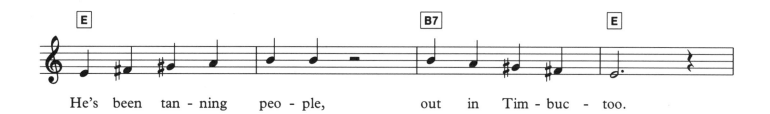

He's been tan - ning peo - ple, out in Tim - buc - too.

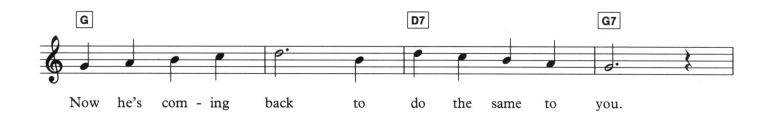

Now he's com - ing back to do the same to you.

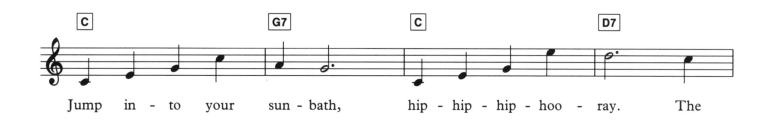

Jump in - to your sun - bath, hip - hip - hip - hoo - ray. The

sun has got his hat on and he's com - ing out to - day.

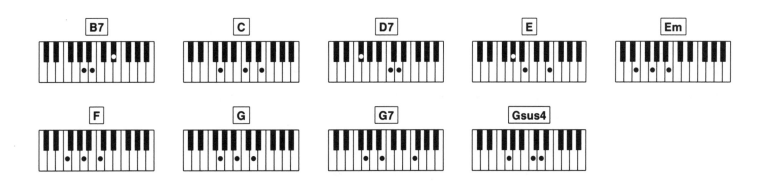

Tomorrow

Words by Martin Charnin / Music by Charles Strouse

Suggested Registration: Piano
Rhythm: 8 beat
Tempo: ♩ = 64

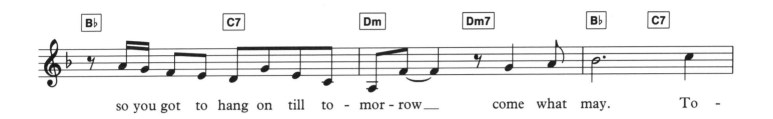

so you got to hang on till to - mor - row___ come what may. To -

- mor-row, to - mor-row, I love ya to - mor-row. You're al - ways a day a -

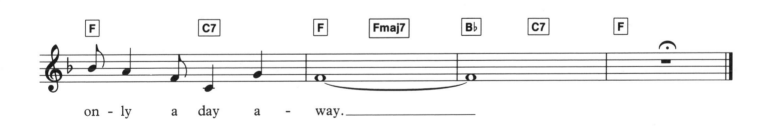

- way. To - mor-row, to - mor-row, I love ya to - mor-row. You're

on - ly a day a - way._____

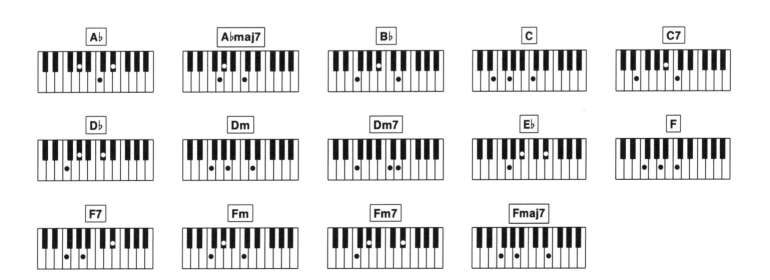

True Love

Words & Music by Cole Porter

Suggested Registration: Acoustic Guitar
Rhythm: Waltz
Tempo: ♩ = 95

Sun tanned, wind blown, hon - ey - moon - ers at

last a - lone. Feel - ing far a - bove par,

oh, how luc - ky we are._____ While I give to you and you

give to me, true love, true love. So

on and on it will al - ways be, true love,

true love. For you and I have a guard - ian an - gel on

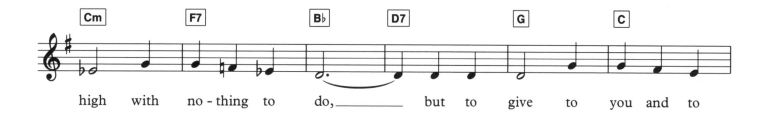

high with no - thing to do,_____ but to give to you and to

give to me love for - ev - er true._____

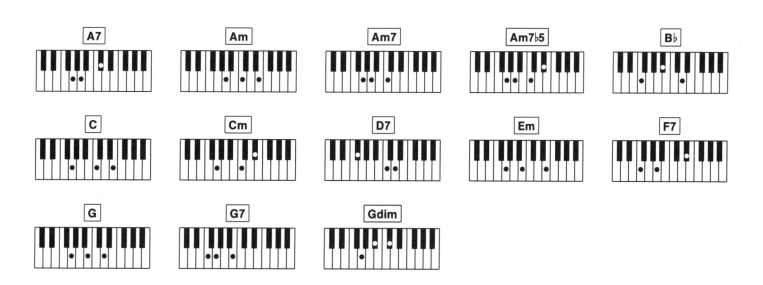

Wand'rin Star

Words by Alan Jay Lerner / Music by Frederick Loewe

Suggested Registration: Acoustic Guitar
Rhythm: Country / Shuffle
Tempo: ♩ = 92

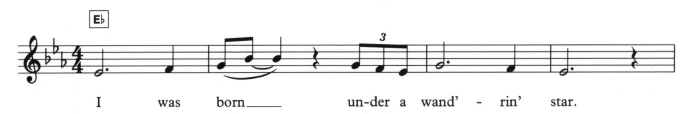

I was born ____ un-der a wand' - rin' star.

I was born ____ un-der a wand' - rin' star.

Do I know where hell is? ____ Hell is in hel - lo.

Hea - ven is good - bye for - ev - er. It's time for me to go.

I was born ____ un - der a wand' - rin'

star, a wand' - rin', wand' - rin' star.

Who Wants To Be A Millionaire?

Words & Music by Cole Porter

Suggested Registration: Piano
Rhythm: Dixie Swing
Tempo: ♩ = 180

Who wants to be a mil - lion - aire? (I don't.)

Have flash - y flunk - eys ev - 'ry - where? (I don't.)

Who wants the both - er of a coun - try es - tate? (A

coun - try es - tate is some - thing I'd hate.)

45

Who wants to wal - low in cham - pagne? (I don't.)

Who wants a su - per - so - nic plane? (I don't.)

Who wants a mar - ble swim - ming pool too? (I don't.) And

I don't 'cause all I want is you._____

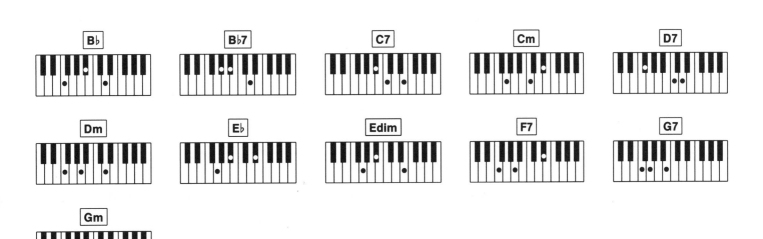

You'll Never Walk Alone

Words by Oscar Hammerstein II / Music by Richard Rodgers

Suggested Registration: Piano
Rhythm: Pop 8 beat
Tempo: ♩ = 88

When you walk through a storm hold your head up

high, and don't be a‑fraid of the dark.

At the end of the storm is a gold‑en

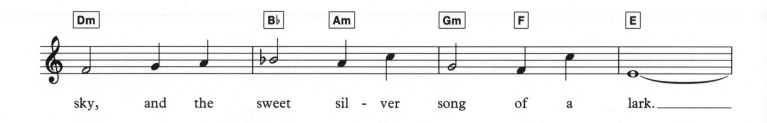

sky, and the sweet sil‑ver song of a lark.

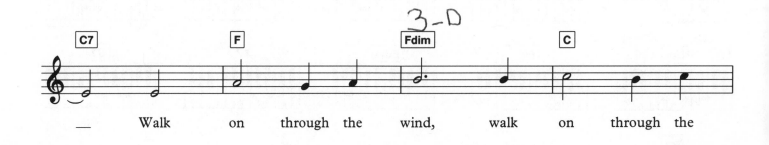

Walk on through the wind, walk on through the

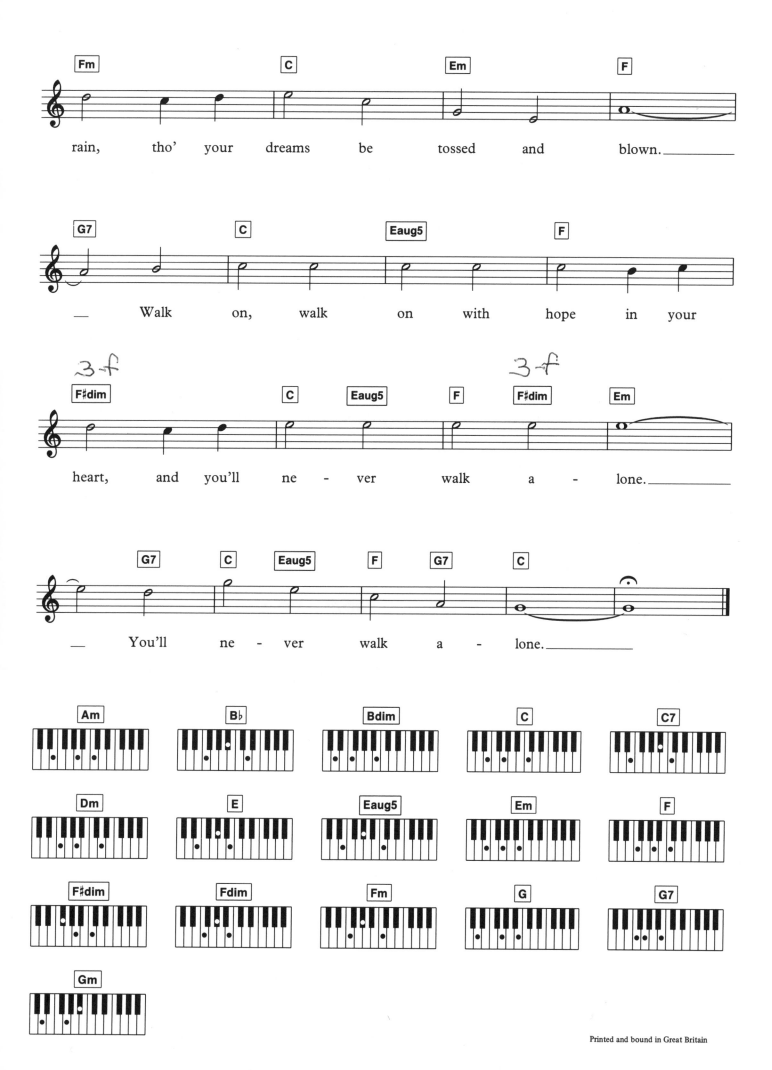

THE EASY KEYBOARD LIBRARY
Also Available In this Series

COUNTRY SONGS FOR KEYBOARD

Always On My Mind	Jealousy	Rhinestone Cowboy
By The Time I Get To Phoenix	Jolene	The Rose
Cry	Just When I Needed You Most	Stand By Your Man
Don't It Make My Brown Eyes Blue	Lady	Tie A Yellow Ribbon
Help Me Make It Through The Night	Leaving On A Jet Plane	'Round The Ole Oak Tree
Honky Tonk Man	Me And Bobby McGee	We've Got Tonight
I'm Gonna Sit Right Down And Write Myself A Letter	Rainy Night In Georgia	The Wind Beneath My Wings
I Never Once Stopped Loving You	Red Sails In The Sunset	You've Got A Friend

BIG BAND HITS FOR KEYBOARD

April In Paris	It Had To Be You	September Song
Avalon	It's Only A Paper Moon	A String Of Pearls
Begin The Beguine	La Vie En Rose	Tea For Two
Come Fly With Me	My Heart Stood Still	Thou Swell
Fly Me To The Moon	Night And Day	Tuxedo Junction
Get Happy	Oh, Lady Be Good!	The Very Thought Of You
Indian Summer	On The Sunny Side Of The Street	What Is This Thing Called Love?
In The Mood	Secret Love	

CLASSIC HITS FOR KEYBOARD VOLUME 1

All Woman	Got My Mind Set On You	Nothing's Gonna Stop Us Now
Coming Around Again	Hanky Panky	The One
Driven By You	I'd Do Anything For Love (But I Won't Do That)	Pray
End Of The Road		Show Me Heaven
Eternal Flame	Like A Prayer	True Colors
From A Distance	Moving On Up	Venus
Get Here	Nobody Does It Better	You're The One That I Want
Go Away	Nothing Compares 2 U	Zoom

CLASSIC HITS FOR KEYBOARD VOLUME 2

Arthur's Theme	The Greatest Love Of All	My Baby Just Cares For Me
Be My Baby	A Groovy Kind Of Love	My Girl
Careless Whisper	Heal The World	Save The Best For Last
Don't Go Breaking My Heart	Hotel California	This Is It
Don't Let The Sun Go Down On Me	I Got You Babe	Up Where We Belong
Drive	I Just Called To Say I Love You	We Are Family
Fever	In All The Right Places	What A Wonderful World
For Your Eyes Only	Mandy	

LOVE SONGS FOR KEYBOARD

Careless Whisper	If	Saving All My Love For You
Close To You (They Long To Be)	I Just Called To Say I Love You	September Song
Crazy For You	It Had To Be You	Show Me Heaven
Embraceable You	Love Is Here To Stay	Talkin' In Your Sleep
The First Time Ever I Saw Your Face	Love Letters	Tonight, I Celebrate My Love For You
Get Here	Mandy	True Love
I'd Do Anything For Love (But I Won't Do That)	My Funny Valentine	The Twelfth Of Never
	A Nightingale Sang In Berkeley Square	When I Fall In Love

THE EASY KEYBOARD LIBRARY